QUEEN'S COUNSEL

QUEEN'S COUNSEL

A Libellous Look at the Law

BY STEUART & FRANCIS

Robson Books

First published in Great Britain in 1995 by Robson Books Ltd, Bolsover House, 5-6 Clipstone Street, London W1P 8LE

British Library Cataloguing in Publication Data
A catalogue record for this title is available from the British Library

ISBN 0 86051 997 X

Printed in Great Britain by WBC Book Manufacturers Ltd, Bridgend, Mid-Glamorgan

The authors would like to thank David Driver, Rosemary Righter, Peter Roberts and Rosemary Canter, without whose efforts this book would not have seen the light of day. Also, thanks to Emma and Flossie for putting up with us during the course of writing it.

As a leading member of the legal profession it is always a pleasure to see oneself and one's colleagues exposed to the revealing mirror of satire. Too often in the past the Bar has reacted defensively to such criticism, and has lacked the collective sense of humour to keep it in its proper perspective. I have no doubt that the authors of this admirable collection of cartoons will take my decision to serve immediate legal proceedings for libel in the humorous spirit in which it is intended.

I wish them every success with their new book (pending the lifting of the injunction).

Sir Geoffrey Brentwood QC

Sir Geoffrey Brentwood QC
4 Lawn Buildings
Temple
EC4

OCTOBER 1943. BARRISTERS VOTE AGAINST THE ABOLITION OF WIGS IN COURT.

NOVEMBER 1993. THE LORD CHIEF JUSTICE APPEARS ON "QUESTION TIME" DURING THE WEEK THAT THE HOME SECRETARY ANNOUNCES PROPOSALS TO MODIFY DEFENDANTS' RIGHT TO SILENCE

DECEMBER 1963. SOLICITORS END BARRISTERS' TRADITIONAL MONOPOLY ON RIGHTS OF AUDIENCE IN THE HIGH COURT.

FANS OF THE ARCHERS WRITE TO THE HOME SECRETARY AFTER ONE OF THE CHARACTERS IS IMPRISONED. JANUARY 1994.

JANUARY 1994. THE WIFE OF JOHN BOBBIT SEVERS HER HUSBAND'S PENIS AFTER AN ARGUMENT.

LLOYDS NAMES REJECT A £100 MILLION OFFER TO SETTLE OUTSTANDING LITIGATION. FEBRUARY 1994.

LAUGHING ALL THE WAY TO THE LLOYDS...

GAY & LESBIAN GROUPS LOBBY PARLIAMENT TO REDUCE THE AGE OF CONSENT TO 16,
IN LINE WITH HETEROSEXUALS. FEBRUARY 1994.

MARCH 1994. HOUSE OF LORDS RULES THAT PART-TIME EMPLOYEES ARE TO ENJOY THE SAME RIGHTS AS THOSE WORKING FULL-TIME.

MARCH 1994. SIR NICHOLAS LYELL, ATTORNEY-GENERAL, IS QUESTIONED BY THE SCOTT ENQUIRY FOR HIS RÔLE IN THE MATRIX CHURCHILL TRIAL.

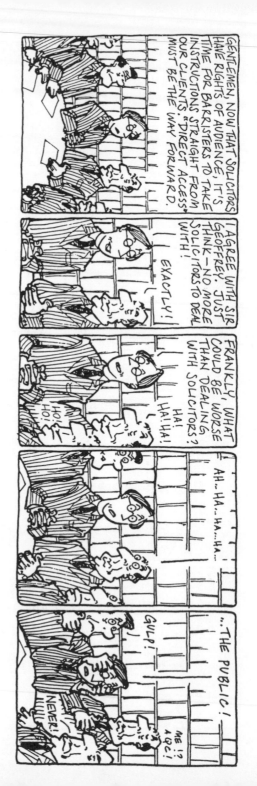

MAY 1994. WIDESPREAD PRESS CRITICISM AS BAR SCHOOL (BARRISTER'S TRAINING COURSE) CHANGES ITS SELECTION CRITERIA SO THAT DEGREE RESULTS ARE NOT TAKEN INTO ACCOUNT.

ARE YOU GOING TO HAVE A GO AT THE LOTTERY, CRISPIN?
I SUPPOSE SO, SIR GEOFFREY.
THOUGH PERSONALLY I THINK IT SHOULD BE A GAME OF SKILL, NOT CHANCE.
BUT THAT'S THE WHOLE POINT CRISPIN!
THE RANDOM ELEMENT MAKES IT FUN! ANYWAY, THERE'S NO LIMIT TO THE NUMBER OF TIMES YOU CAN APPLY.
I'M SURE YOU'LL BECOME A QC ONE OF THESE DAYS...
WELL, AFTER 8 TRIES IT GETS FRANKLY EMBARASSING...

JUNE 6TH 1994. THE 50TH ANNIVERSARY OF THE D-DAY LANDINGS IS REMEMBERED.

I MUST SAY YOUR CHAMBERS LOOKS VERY IMPRESSIVE, SIR GEOFFREY – ALL THAT MARBLE AND POLISHED STEEL.
– THANKYOU, MR SPROCKET.
QUITE PALATIAL REALLY. YOU MUST BE DOING VERY WELL.
WE LIKE TO THINK SO.
WHO PAYS FOR IT ALL, I WONDER?
ER...
AHEM!
COUGH!
COUGH!
IF WE MIGHT MOVE ON TO THE DETAILS OF YOUR CASE, MR SPROCKET.

JULY 1994. THE LORD CHANCELLOR'S DEPARTMENT ISSUES A PRACTICE DIRECTION PREVENTING SOLICITOR–ADVOCATES FROM WEARING WIGS IN COURT.

IN MY DAY, EDWARD, INSIDER DEALING WASN'T EVEN AN OFFENCE. ALL THE CITY BOYS WERE AT IT.
ARCHER CLEARED OF INSIDER DEALING
THOUGH I, LIKE SO MANY LAWYERS, WORKED HARD TO HAVE THE LAW CHANGED.
PEOPLE SAY IT'S A VICTIMLESS CRIME, BUT THERE WERE PEOPLE OUT THERE SUFFERING!
LIKE WHO, EXACTLY?
ME, FOR ONE. I DIDN'T HAVE ACCESS TO INSIDE INFORMATION!
QUITE RIGHT—BANKERS EARN TOO MUCH ANYWAY.

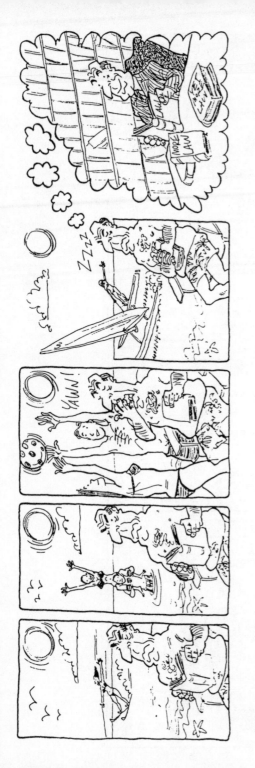

HELENA, THIS DOCUMENT YOU DRAFTED IS PEDANTIC IN THE EXTREME.
IT'S UNECESSARILY LONG, PACKED WITH REDUNDANT CLAUSES, AND HAS MORE FOOTNOTES THAN AN ACADEMIC TREATISE.
IT COVERS A MULTITUDE OF CONTINGENCIES SO REMOTE THEY SEEM BARELY WORTH CONSIDERING!
I COULDN'T HAVE DONE IT BETTER MYSELF!
I... DID MY BEST...

THE LORD CHANCELLOR'S DEPARTMENT DECIDES TO ADVERTISE FOR DISTRICT & CIRCUIT JUDGES. OCTOBER 1994.

...IN CONCLUSION, GENTLEMEN, I REJECT THE MASTER OF THE ROLLS'S ACCUSATION THAT BARRISTERS SPEAK TOO LONG AND DELAY THE COURSE OF JUSTICE.

IT IS A SLUR ON OUR PROFESSION, AN ASSAULT ON OUR DIGNITY...

...AND WILL NEVER BE TOLERATED BY RIGHT-THINKING MEMBERS OF THE BAR.

ARE THERE ANY QUESTIONS? ZZZ ZZZZZ

THE MASTER OF THE ROLLS URGES BARRISTERS TO BE MORE CONCISE IN COURT. OCTOBER 1994.

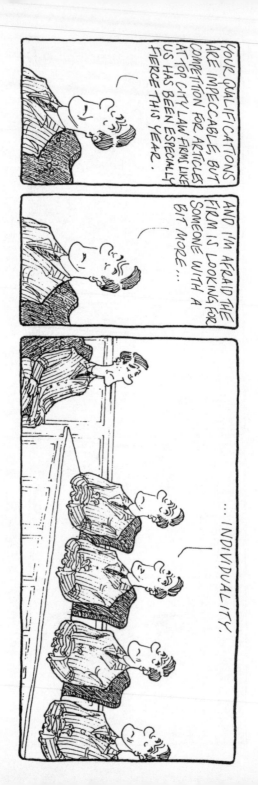

TWO CONSERVATIVE MPs ARE REVEALED TO HAVE ACCEPTED CASH FROM THE SUNDAY TIMES TO ASK PARLIAMENTARY QUESTIONS. OCTOBER 1994.

DADDY'S HAD A HARD WEEK SITTING AS A RECORDER IN THE CROWN COURT. TRY NOT TO PROVOKE HIM, DARLING.
OK, MUM.
DADDY, CAN I BORROW A FIVER?
HMPH! WHAT DO YOU SAY?
PLEASE? PRETTY PLEASE?
PROD
BEST DADDY IN THE WORLD?
HMF!
TUG
YOUR HONOUR?
THAT'S BETTER.
£5

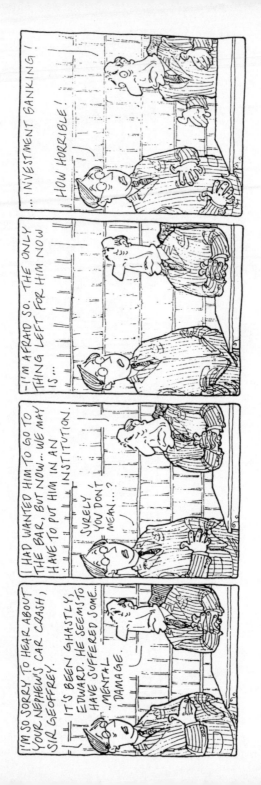

DAMIEN HIRST EXHIBITS A PICKLED SHEEP AT THE WHITECHAPEL GALLERY.

JANUARY 1995. SOLICITOR ACCUSED OF "GREEN FORM" LEGAL AID FRAUD, AS THE LORD CHANCELLOR ANNOUNCES PLANS FOR A CAP IN THE LEGAL AID BUDGET.

JANUARY 1995. LORD LESTER QC RESIGNS FROM THE GARRICK IN PROTEST AT THE CONTINUED BAN ON WOMEN MEMBERS.

JANUARY 1996 — OJ SIMPSON'S LAWYERS COMPLAIN THAT A FAIR TRIAL IS IMPOSSIBLE DUE TO MEDIA SPECULATION OVER THE OUTCOME OF THE CASE.

FEBRUARY 1996 – MAXWELL BROTHERS RECEIVE MILLIONS OF POUNDS IN LEGAL AID TO DEFEND FRAUD CHARGES

NICK LEESON, A DERIVATIVES TRADER AT BARINGS BANK IN SINGAPORE, PRECIPITATES THE DOWNFALL OF ONE OF THE CITY'S OLDEST INSTITUTIONS. MARCH 1995.

MAY 1995. PROPOSALS FOR REFORM OF DIVORCE LAWS TO END "QUICKIE" DIVORCES.

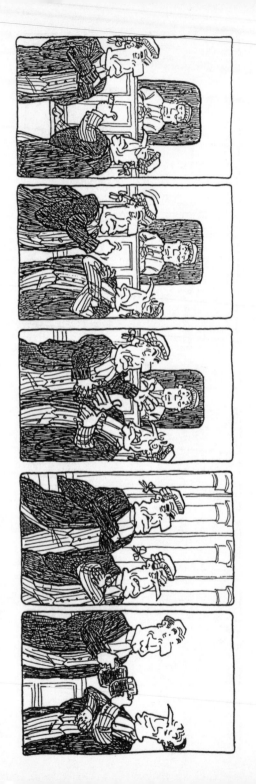

MAY 1996. FEMALE BARRISTERS ALLEGE WIDESPREAD SEXUAL HARASSMENT AT THE BAR.

I CAN'T SEE HOW COMPULSORY RETIREMENT FOR JUDGES AT 70 CAN POSSIBLY BE JUSTIFIED.
YOU AND I STILL HAVE 10 GOOD YEARS ON THE BENCH LEFT IN US.
THE JUDGMENT REPORTED HERE IS ONE OF MY FINEST EVER!
BUT HUMPHREY...
...THAT WAS IN 1973
WELL, IT SEEMS LIKE YESTERDAY TO ME.
TIME FOR YOUR LUNCH, YOUR WORSHIPS.

DIVINE BROWN, THE HOLLYWOOD PROSTITUTE LINKED WITH HUGH GRANT, SELLS HER STORY TO THE NEWS OF THE WORLD. JULY 1995.

CONTROVERSY SURROUNDS THE PROSECUTION OF FORMER NAZIS FOR WAR CRIMES. JULY 1995.